EMMA

by Cheryl Wills

Illustrated by Sue Cornelison

Sussman Education/Lightswitch Learning
250 East 54th Street, Suite P2
New York, NY 10022

www.lightswitchlearning.com

250 East 54th Street, Suite P2

New York, NY 10022

www.lightswitchlearning.com

Educators and Librarians, for a variety of teaching resources, visit www.lightswitchlearning.com.

Library of Congress Cataloging-in-Publication Data is available upon request.

ISBN: 978-1-68265-642-6

Emma by Cheryl Wills

Edited by Adam Reingold

Art Direction and Book Design by Paula Jo Smith

The text of this book is set in Futura.

Printed in Dominican Republic

To my great-great-great grandmother,
Emma West Moore Wills, circa 1851–1901,

Your home state of Tennessee forgot you.
Even most of your family forgot you.
But I will make sure the world remembers
that you were here and you made an impact!

Introduction

My great-great-great grandmother Emma Wills's story was one of the lost stories of the Civil War Era (1861–1865) until I unearthed it. As near as I can tell, this story is true. I pieced it together from historical records about my family before and after the war in Haywood County, Tennessee. Like most family histories, there are gaps, so I used my knowledge of the time and place to imagine Emma's transition from an enslaved girl to a free woman.

Emma at age 10

Emma's bondage is an uncommon story. Even though Emma's father was enslaved, he had privileges on the plantation that few other enslaved people had, and those privileges extended to his wife and children. My great-great-great grandmother Emma grew up working in the home of John Bertie Moore and his wife, and Emma was well acquainted with the couple's privileged children, Joel, Sally, and John.

Emma was a brave girl who lived in America during a painful period. I hope her legacy inspires readers to continue to stand up for what they believe is important.

Haywood County, Tennessee, 1858

Emma knew she was different. Other slaves worked Master's fields. But she took pride in caring for his children. Her chores waited while she galloped stick ponies with Young Master Joel and played dolls with his little sister Sally.

"Was this what freedom felt like?" she wondered.

When the tutor came to teach Young Master Joel and Miss Sally, Mrs. Moore sent Emma back to her chores. But Emma listened in when Mrs. Moore wasn't looking and dared to dream.

"Teach me reading and writing,"
Emma whispered to Young Master Joel
one day after his lessons. Together,
they traced forbidden letters
in the dirt.

"Son, come inside now," Mrs.
Moore called at the same time
Mother said, "Help me carry
these pecans, child."

Emma heard the echo of trouble between their words.

"You want a whipping from Master Moore?" Mother whispered. "Colored folks aren't supposed to read and write. You're old enough now to see the truth of it."

Emma already knew the sorry truth. Freedom. Reading. Writing. Three forbidden dreams. Master Moore whipped anyone who dared disobey, and then he sold their families to other plantations.

Because Poppa ran Master Moore's cotton plantation, Master never whipped or sold Poppa's family. Emma knew she belonged to Master Moore, but Poppa's position protected her.

6

8

And Emma dared to help other slave children. When one slave girl broke Mrs. Moore's teacup, Emma took the blame.

When Mother was allowed to take leftover pork from the white folks' kitchen, Emma shared her portion with the slave children who worked the fields. And she dared to ask Young Master Joel to teach her to read and write again.

"You know I can't, Emma," he whispered.

"It ain't right," she said.

By 1861, sounds of civil war echoed in the sweltering air. North fought South. Cannon fire shook the house. Soldiers marched beside the Hatchie River as it crossed the plantation. "President Lincoln and the North gonna free us, child," Mother said to Emma.

For four long years, Emma hid a
handful of hope in her heart. Maybe a
free girl could learn to read and write.

When the South finally surrendered in 1865, the walls of slavery came tumbling down.

Emma and her family were free at last. For the first time in their lives, they belonged to each other and no one else.

Poppa and Mother stayed to farm a plot of Moore land for pay.

"It's all we know," Poppa said.

Emma grew taller as her family grew larger. She minded her younger brothers and sisters and fretted because the tutor never came to the farm anymore. Her dream of reading and writing withered.

Instead, she told the children stories of heroes and sang songs of freedom to make them strong.

One day, an army man named Sandy Wills came to ask Poppa for a job. Emma followed this strong, handsome war hero with her eyes. More than once, she caught him peepin' at her.

They married in 1869. Not in the field as most slaves used to, but in the white folks' house with Joel Moore's blessing.

Emma's eyes sparkled. Sandy stood tall.

White and colored guests celebrated the first official colored folks' marriage on the Moore plantation.

Sandy signed his mark on the marriage license. They couldn't read it, but it was proof they were married.

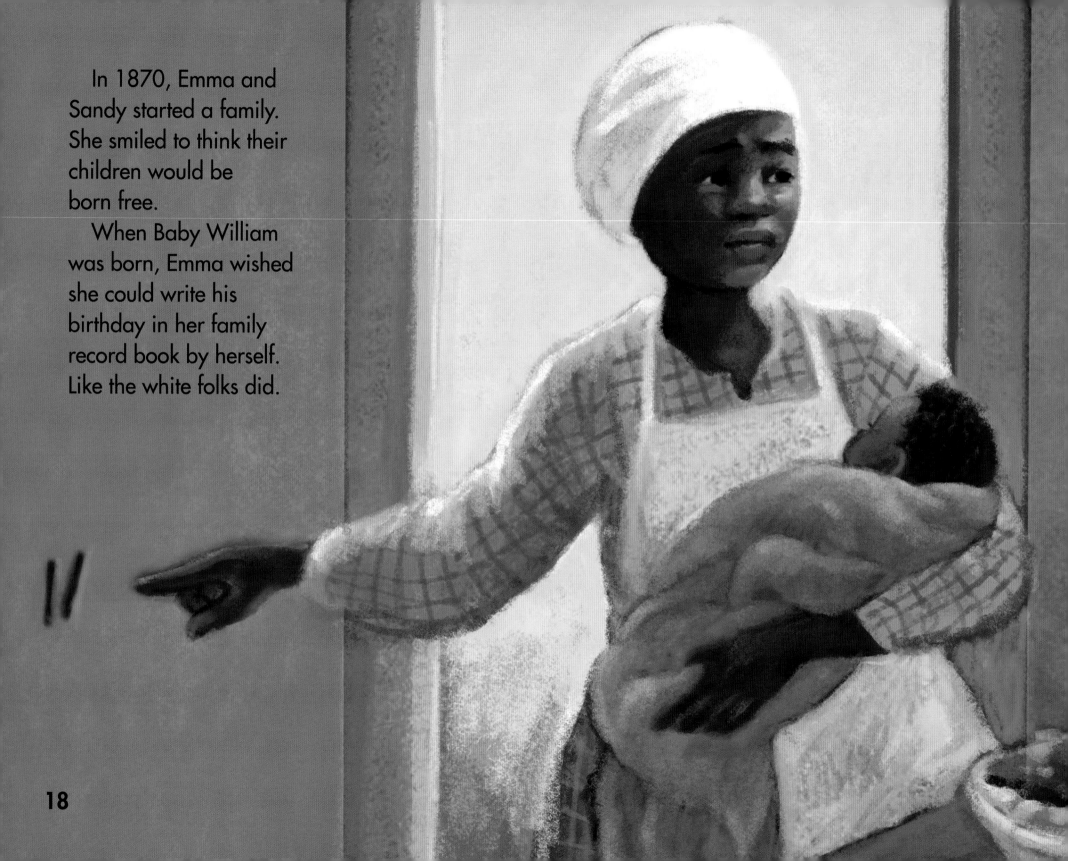

In 1870, Emma and Sandy started a family. She smiled to think their children would be born free.

When Baby William was born, Emma wished she could write his birthday in her family record book by herself. Like the white folks did.

18

Instead, she waited for Joel Moore to visit the farm.

"My child will grow up knowing his birthday, sir," Emma said.

"We all have birthdays," Joel Moore said.

"Not us former slaves," Emma replied. "My son was born that many days ago." She pointed to the marks on the wall.

19

Seven more children followed. Each time, Emma gave Joel Moore a pecan pie. "My children will grow up knowing their birthdays, sir."

Each time Emma watched him record a new birth in the book, she fought back tears because she couldn't write the names herself.

Sometimes, a teacher came by to teach Emma and Sandy's children. Emma's faded dream rebloomed for her children.

20

But a few years later,
in 1889, everything changed.
Emma cried a year of tears.

Tears of sadness for the loss
of her beloved Sandy.

Tears bitter and sweet for Baby
James born a month later.

Tears of worry for her nine fatherless
children. For the first time in her life,
Emma felt helpless.

Emma and her children kept farming, but they never had enough money after Sandy died. Some folks told her the government had set aside money for former soldiers and their families.

"Colored soldiers too?" she wondered. She dared to apply.

24

"My Sandy fought for my freedom and for these
United States," Emma said to Joel Moore the next time
he visited the farm. "Will you send the government his
honorable Army discharge?"
Emma waited and waited.

DENIED! the government replied
because the discharge papers said Sandy's
last name was Willis instead of Wills.

Emma knew from experience that fighting
for her rights would not be easy. She gathered
her courage and tried again.

"Please send my marriage license," she told
Joel Moore. "Sandy signed it with his mark
over twenty years ago."

Emma waited and waited.

DENIED! the government replied because the marriage license said Sandy's last name was Williams instead of Wills.

"I'm sorry, Emma," Joel Moore said. "We've done all we can do."

Emma hid her anger and frustration. "There must be something more."

28

The answer came to her as she hugged
her family record book.

"Joel Moore, please send the government
the birth records of my nine children
written in your fine hand," she said. "They
prove Sandy was their father."

Emma waited and waited.

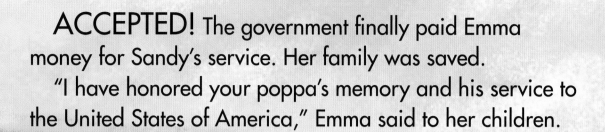

ACCEPTED! The government finally paid Emma
money for Sandy's service. Her family was saved.
   "I have honored your poppa's memory and his service to
the United States of America," Emma said to her children.

Today

Emma died more than 100 years ago, but her dreams of reading and writing left an unforgettable mark on her family. I know because I'm her great-great-great granddaughter.

Emma's children learned to read because of their mother. If I could give her one gift, I'd show her how to finally write her own name.

Primary Source

Primary sources are pieces of information like letters, photos, and documents created by someone who was part of a past event. Just like detectives, people can look at clues and evidence in these sources to better understand people and events long ago.

To write this book, the author used primary sources to help her learn more about her family's life long ago.

What primary sources have you read or looked at to learn more about your own family's history?

In what ways were the following primary sources useful in enabling the author to write this book?

This painting shows John Bertie Moore, the slave master who owned Emma and her family.

This photo shows a slave's home from the same plantation that Emma and her family lived on long ago.

This marriage certificate shows that Emma and Sandy were married on January 25, 1869.

Depth of Knowledge

DISCUSSION QUESTIONS

1. Explain how Emma found inner strength to empower her family.

2. Emma wants to learn how to read and write, but she isn't allowed to. Is this fair? Explain.

3. When thinking of slavery, President Abraham Lincoln said, "Those who deny freedom to others, deserve it not for themselves." What did he mean by this statement?

4. What do you think the slaves felt when they saw Master Moore whipping a slave? Explain.

5. Emma takes the blame when one of the slave girls breaks a teacup. Why do you think she did this? Would you ever do this for a friend?

6. The author writes, "Emma hid a handful of hope in her heart." What does she mean?

7. When the slaves were set free, Emma's mother and father decided to stay and work for Mr. Moore. Why did they do this?

8. Describe what it might feel like to be set free after being a slave. What are some of the first things you would do as a free person?

9. Emma was responsible for taking care of her younger brothers and sisters. Do you have any responsibilities at home?

10. On page 26, the author writes that Emma "gathered her courage and tried again." Describe a time when you had to have courage. What did you do?

11. The government initially denied Emma's request for money to support her family several times. Describe a time when you tried something many times before you achieved your goals.

12. Do you think Emma is an inspiration to her family and others today? Include details to support your conclusion.

ACTIVITIES

1. Emma dreams of being able to read and write. Write your own story about a person who has a dream. Discuss if the dream came true or not.

2. Emma keeps a family record book. Create your own record book that includes the date you were born, where you live, your favorite things to do, primary sources, and anything else that's important in your life.

3. On page 12, the author writes that "the walls of slavery came tumbling down." Draw a picture to describe what the author means.

4. Write a poem describing Emma's emotions when her family was finally set free.

5. Emma told her children that she honored their father's memory. Write a paragraph to honor someone who means a lot to you.

6. Write a diary entry from the point of view of a slave near the end of the Civil War. Describe what you've seen and felt as well as the things you hope will happen after the war is over.

GROUP ACTIVITY
Gallery Walk

Have students work together in small groups to discuss key concepts presented in the book, such as equality, literacy, and freedom.

Step 1: Create five questions for each central concept, and write them on a piece of chart paper for each station.

Step 2: At each station, have students read, discuss, and respond to the questions and prompts posted. Have each group assign a recorder to write down each group's thoughts.

Step 3: After five minutes, have the groups rotate to the next station.

Step 4: Monitor the groups as they discuss and write their thoughts.

Step 5: After each group has visited each station, have every student in each group discuss what was learned and discussed at each station.

Glossary

Acquainted *(adjective)* knowing someone *(p.1)*

Apply *(verb)* to make a request *(p. 24)*

Bitter *(adjective)* hard to accept *(p. 23)*

Blessing *(noun)* approval *(p. 16)*

Bondage *(noun)* being a slave *(p. 1)*

Chores *(noun)* small jobs or tasks *(p. 3)*

Civil War *(noun)* a war fought from 1861–1865 in the United States between people who lived in the North and people who lived in the South *(p. 1)*

Colored *(adjective)* an old term for a person who isn't white; now considered offensive *(p. 5)*

Denied *(verb)* to refuse to give something to someone *(p. 26)*

Discharge *(noun)* dismissal from a position in the military *(p. 25)*

Disobey *(verb)* to refuse to do or to obey *(p. 6)*

Echo *(noun)* the repeating of a sound *(p. 5)*

Enslaved *(verb)* to make someone a slave *(p. 1)*

Era *(noun)* a period of time *(p. 1)*

Family record book *(noun)* a book used to keep track of the names, birth dates, and other important information for all of the members of a family *(p. 18)*

Forbidden *(adjective)* not allowed *(p. 4)*

Former *(adjective)* having been something in the past *(p. 19)*

Freedom *(noun)* the power to do what you want to do *(p. 3)*

Fretted *(verb)* to worry *(p. 14)*

Frustration *(noun)* feeling of anger *(p. 28)*

Galloped *(verb)* to run fast *(p. 3)*

Honored *(verb)* to treat with respect and admiration *(p. 31)*

Legacy (*noun*) something handed down from an ancestor (*p. 1*)

License (*noun*) an official document (*p. 17*)

Mark (*noun*) a cross made in place of a signature (*p. 17*)

Master (*noun*) someone who has power and control over slaves (*p. 3*)

Minded (*verb*) taking charge of (*p. 14*)

Pecans (*noun*) a kind of nut (*p. 4*)

Peepin' (*verb*) to look at (*p. 16*)

Plantation (*noun*) a large property where slaves often lived and worked (*p. 1*)

Plot (*noun*) a small area of land for farming (*p. 12*)

Portion (*noun*) serving of a meal (*p. 9*)

Position (*noun*) job (*p. 6*)

Primary sources (*noun*) pieces of information like letters, photos, and documents created by someone who was part of an event from the past (*p. 34*)

Privileges (*noun*) special treatment (*p. 1*)

Rebloomed (*verb*) to come back or rise up again (*p. 20*)

Slaves (*noun*) individuals who are owned by another person and forced to work (*p.3*)

Surrendered (*verb*) to give in to someone or something with more power (*p. 12*)

Sweltering (*adjective*) very hot (*p. 10*)

Transition (*noun*) changing from one thing to another (*p. 1*)

Tutor (*noun*) a special teacher (*p. 3*)

Whipping (*noun*) hitting a slave to punish him or her (*p. 5*)

Withered (*verb*) to lose excitement and enthusiasm (*p. 14*)

Acknowledgments

This book is a love letter to every woman who raised me and shaped me from birth until this present day.

Ever since I learned about my great-great-great grandmother Emma's extraordinary journey from circa 1851 to 1901, I have witnessed her strength within all the important mothers in my life—beginning with the strong lady whom I call "Mommy," my dear mother, Ruth. When my father died in 1980 at an untimely early age (38), much like Emma, Ruth became both a mother and a father to me and my brothers and sisters. She battled to keep all five of us in a stable household during a very unstable period—with little disruption in our lives. Ruth succeeded. Her five babies survived the tumultuous 1980s, and we are now each successful in our own way.

When it comes to Ruth, every day is Mother's Day!

My maternal grandmother Sallie (1908–1992) and my paternal grandmother Opal (b. 1927), lived remarkably similar lives. Both were granddaughters of enslaved women who abandoned their southern roots in South Carolina and Tennessee, respectively, for better lives in New York City. With limited education, they took the only jobs available to them as domestics and married young and raised their children. Like Emma, they had a tenacious grip on their households and ruled with love and discipline.

My literary agent, Lois de la Haba is someone with motherly wit whom I absolutely adore as a member of my extended family. Like Emma, she has a fearlessness and determination that can't be beat!

I'm also deeply grateful to Lois for being part of the editing team for this empowering book.

Literary agents like Lois are incredibly hard to come by, and I'm eternally grateful to my beautiful sister-friend Patty Danko for connecting us.

My sincere thanks also to Paula Jo Smith for overseeing the design and layout of this book. I will miss our conference calls. You are a woman of excellence, and it was an honor to collaborate with you on this project.

Alas, I cannot leave out the gentlemen who were also instrumental in publishing Emma's story.

My editor Adam Reingold and I are like peanut butter and jelly at this point. We read each other's minds. We understand each other's points, and we finish each other's sentences! I'm grateful to have you in my life.

This is my fourth book with Ron and Steve Sussman at Sussman Education. They took a chance on me and published my first children's book, *The Emancipation of Grandpa Sandy Wills*, when no one else would. Over the years, we've provided thousands of books to students who are always eager to learn more. Thank you for paving the way by publishing culturally diverse biographies—it's desperately needed. Bravo!

Cheryl